This Manual
Is Written In GOLD
To Stress The
Importance Of Looking After
Your Body, Mind And Life Properly,
And The Importance
Of Learning To Use Them Wisely

Written by Marvin Sawyer and Joyce Sawyer B.Ed.

Contributors:

> Donna Nicol, Angelen VanDaele, B.A.
> Dorothy Galyean, Pat Wong,
> and Denise Shepherd.

Printed in Canada

Copyright © 1996, 1998, 2000 A & S Human Development Inc.
ISBN 0-96817-800-6

Published by A & S Human Development Inc.

USA address:
> 8163 E. Mercer Ln.
> Scottsdale, AZ
> 85260 USA

Canadian address:
> 14316 - 63 Avenue
> Edmonton, AB
> T6H 1S4 Canada

Prologue

To acquaint you with the Personal Manual For The Young, please glance through the Table of Contents, the short, one page introduction, the list of Resolutions For The Next Century in the "Future" chapter, and the body maintenance journal (records).

Manuals are not meant to be thrillers, but are a NECESSITY to make even simple machines function without problems for many years - the live sophisticated Human Machine is no EXCEPTION. The following is something that all of us should remember.

"How To Live" for The Young is a common sense "Overview of Life" with a mini guide to Living and a Life style Journal directed at young teens and their parents. It uses a theme of Gold and a simple basic approach to enhance your chances of living a healthier, safer and fuller life.

Young people often take their health and life for granted without realizing that the best time to learn good healthy habits and attitudes is at an early age. Only when they grow older, do they appreciate the fact that life and Good Health are very priceless gifts.

More information and international testimonials and acknowledgements can be seen on website www.howtolive.com.

Because Canada and the USA are closely related in many aspects some American and some Canadian content is used in terms of Statistics and Surveys.

Contents

Chapter Three – THE MAGIC OF EXERCISE

Facts

Statistics

Chapter Four – PREVENTION

Vaccines

Discipline

Good Health Habits

Protection From The Sun

Chapter Five – SAFETY

Home Accidents

Walking Tips

Cycling Tips

Motorcycle Facts

Auto Safety

Swimming

First Aid

Safety Statistics

Chapter Six – MENTAL HEALTH

Living A Balanced Life

Laughter

Depression

Chapter Nine – PROBLEMS OF OUR TIME

Chapter Ten – THE FUTURE

Chapter Eleven – RECORDS

The world is abound with knowledge and experience. It is known as "information overload." For that reason, this manual is a very condensed, plain language overview of life. It is meant to serve as a mini guide of useful information.

Although we know better, we often take our health and life for granted. Now, when you are young, is the time to learn good, healthy attitudes and habits. This endeavor will reward you through adulthood and last for a lifetime. To attain this goal you need to understand your body, your environment and the many and various problems of your era.

You also need to know the results of bad habits and actions. Then you can learn how to manage and control your behavior in a positive manner, so as to steer you on a solid course for future good health, happiness and lasting love. Unfortunately, it is sometimes difficult to realize the cost that bad habits or actions impose on you, your family and the rest of society.

Best wishes for a successful, happy and long life from former peers and now Graduates of "The School of Life" that we all attend.

Sincerely,

Marv and Joyce Sawyer

Marv and Joyce Sawyer

CHAPTER ONE

THE HUMAN BODY

A GIFT MORE VALUABLE
THAN GOLD

"How To Live" is a Mini Manual to a sweepstakes for the Young where there are no losers. Learning good health habits, proper exercise, prevention and safety makes everyone a winner of prizes with incalculable values. In addition large cash savings will be automatically won by those who stay away from smoking, illegal drugs or a teenage pregnancy. As a bonus prize – a list of **SOLID GOLD RESOLUTIONS FOR THE NEXT CENTURY.**
To become a winner you will need these Free requirements:
Time • Common Sense • Wisdom • WILLPOWER

• *Marvin and Joyce Sawyer* •

My idea of exercise—is to eat faster.
Jackie Gleason

___

Safety
Being told things for our own good, seldom does us any, unless we practice what we are told.

(The Furrow)

___

Life without a friend - is like a desert without an oasis.
Ella W. Wilcox

Cells

- Cells are the unique building blocks of our body systems, that together make up the **MIRACLE** that is a living human being. Healthy cells in properly maintained systems usually create a healthy, strong body.

- The cell is the fundamental unit of life. It is the smallest structure of the body capable of performing all the processes that define life, including respiration, movement, digestion and reproduction. Most cells are so small that they are invisible to the naked eye.

- Your whole body depends on a constant supply of blood to sustain, nourish and protect its cells and tissues. Its respiratory job is to carry oxygen to all the cells. Scientists estimate that an adult will have approximately 25 trillion red blood cells to transport oxygen. Blood also has nutrients dissolved in it, including sugars, amino acids, fatty acids, fats, minerals, vitamins and is a vehicle for transporting information in the form of hormones.

- The data of heredity is carried by complex DNA molecules that tell the body how to grow. The DNA molecules with all the necessary knowledge are crammed into the nucleus of each and every cell and when new cells are born all this knowledge is passed on to them.

• **Something you should know - supplying the cells of your body with (cough, cough) impure oxygen or drug contaminated nutrients may interfere with the precision chemical, organ messages of the hormones or the DNA information for new cell reproduction.**

• **Studying body health in school sporadically over several years may not be as effective as reading a current book in your local library on how the human body is constructed and how it works.**

The Skeletal System

Babies are born with about 350 bones. Adults may only have 206 to 208 bones since some of the original bones fuse together during growth.

Bones form the framework of your body. They give you stature, protect your inner organs and allow you to move.

Your bones are as strong as steel and light as aluminum, however, they are still flexible and blood flows through every part of them.

Red and white cells grow in the inner bone tissue. This is known as bone marrow.

Bones are made of collagen (a protein) and minerals. Many minerals (especially calcium, phosphorous, and small amounts of magnesium), fluorine, chlorine and iron are stored in bone marrow. These components are constantly being removed and replaced as the body needs them.

Cartilage covers the ends of the bones where they move at the joints. Cartilage is made mostly of collagen.

Ligaments are the strong bands of fibrous tissue that link and stabilize the moveable joints.

Tendons, in the form of fibers, tie muscle to the bone. They too, are made of almost pure collagen.

Maintenance

1. Eat a balanced diet that includes adequate amounts of calcium.

2. Exercise regularly.

3. Learn correct posture—walking or sitting.

4. Learn how to lift correctly to protect your back. Never bend from the waist. Always bend the knees and keep your back straight and stomach muscles tense.

5. If you use a computer, set it at the proper height and use a chair with good back support. Back injuries are very common in sedentary jobs.

The Muscular System

The muscular system makes up about half of your body bulk. Muscles are responsible for all body movement. They also maintain posture and generate heat.

There are three groups of muscles that work with the skeletal system and the voluntary and involuntary systems in your body. These muscle groups make it possible for all the systems to function.

Voluntary, or skeletal muscles, are those that allow you to make precise and intricate hand movements, lift objects and speak. Involuntary, or smooth muscles, provide the essential power for your respiratory, digestive and circulatory systems. Cardiac muscles, found in the heart, are the third type.

Muscles depend on a healthy nervous system to give them the feedback and instructions they need.

Muscles are more often injured than diseased and therefore, they can repair themselves. If one muscle is partially destroyed, the remaining part will grow larger and stronger to compensate.

Maintenance

1. Exercise all muscles regularly. Be sure to warm up before you start your workout.

2. Use stretching exercises to warm up.

3. Learn to lift correctly.

4. Try to maintain good posture while standing, sitting or walking. Use a mirror to look at the curvature of your spine.

5. Eat a balanced diet.

6. Try to be involved in less strenuous sports that you can continue through to adulthood.

The Cardiovascular System

The main function of the cardiovascular system is to move blood (the carrying fluid) through your body.

This is done by pumping blood through the arteries and capillaries. Blood has two functions. First, it contains the oxygen and food for all cells. Second, it removes the carbon dioxide and waste from the cells.

Depending on your size, the volume of blood in females is 3 to 5 liters. In males, the volume is 4 to 6 liters.

Blood helps maintain body temperatures and a balance between acidity and alkalinity in body tissues.

Blood has a viscosity three times that of water. About one half of its volume is made up of plasma, that carries digested food, hormones and enzymes to the various cells in your body. The remainder is made up of red, white, and clotting cells.

Red cells get their color from the iron in the hemoglobin. These cells carry oxygen to other cells and remove carbon dioxide from them.

There are five kinds of white cells. Some white cells clear up infections, while others are specifically involved in responding to invasion by germs.

Platelets, or clotting cells, enable your blood to clot on the surface of your skin.

Blood, laden with food and oxygen, is initially pumped through your body via arteries and capillaries. Then it returns, or is pumped back, via your veins and venules. On the return trip, it carries carbon dioxide to the lungs, and wastes to the kidneys and other organs for removal and cleansing.

This pumping action, or circulation of blood, is done by the heart (a powerful muscle). The heart is about the size of your fist. It lies at the front of your chest, slightly to the left.

The heart has several compartments and valves. These features enable the heart to circulate blood. First it pumps blood, under pressure, through arteries and capillaries. Then it receives the blood back, into a compartment that has no pressure, through veins and venules. This cycle is repeated over and over.

To accomplish the circulation process, your heart beats 65 to 75 times a minute. Normal blood pressure in a healthy, young male is about 120/75 and 115/70 in a young female.

Maintenance

1. Do not smoke. Smoking is one of the main causes of heart disease. If you are a smoker, try to stop. It may take several attempts to quit—don't give up!

2. Eat a balanced diet, low in fats, with plenty of fruits and vegetables.

3. Check out your "desired weight" with a doctor and try to maintain it.

4. Watch your calories. It is easier to control your weight this way than by dieting.

5. Develop a good exercise program to help control your weight and alleviate stress. This is very important, especially since school and many jobs are sedentary in nature.

6. Have regular medical examinations.

7. Laughter is a good stress reliever. Don't forget how to laugh. This will help you maintain a good sense of humor as you grow older.

The Nervous System

The nervous system is a sophisticated electrical and chemical system that directly, or indirectly, runs all your body functions. It encompasses your brain, spinal cord, and an elaborate nerve network.

The brain is the most important part of the nervous system. Although weighing only about three pounds, it consists of a conglomeration of several billion inter-connecting cells.

The brain is phenomenal. It can send, receive and store information. It also gives you sight, sound, movement, speech and memory and allows you to experience touch, taste and smell.

Besides running all bodily functions, the brain allows you to reason, have emotions and be creative. In addition, it processes all incoming information so appropriate responses occur.

Like a computer, the part of the brain that you have control over needs "programming." How you "program" it will make a difference in your personality, character, and the successes and failures in your life.

You do not always have control over your inherited character traits, ethnicity, or the examples provided by family and community. However, you can control the "programming" of your brain. The books you read, the education you seek, the music you learn to enjoy, the TV you watch, and the people you choose as friends all influence this "programming" process.

The brain has a tremendous capacity, but on average only seven percent of this capacity is used.

Maintenance

1. Eat balanced meals.

2. Exercise your body regularly.

3. Exercise your brain regularly. Do crossword puzzles or learn how to play chess or bridge. Studying is a good exercise, but try to learn some exercises that will keep your brain active after you leave school.

4. Learn to appreciate good music, good books, or maybe a good TV program.

5. Have a sense of humor. Don't forget how to laugh.

6. Be positive about life. Count your blessings. Do not dwell on your troubles because they usually go away.

The Respiratory System

The respiratory system is the mechanism that exchanges gases throughout your body.

The lungs fill with air about every five seconds. They contract and expel air and carbon dioxide that your body cannot use. This is done with the help of your diaphragm and specific rib muscles that apply and lower pressure against the lungs.

Breathing is something you can control if you want to, however, normally it is automatic.

The hemoglobin in the red blood cells carries oxygen to the cells of various tissues. This oxygen is released according to the tissues' requirements.

Carbon dioxide and water are waste products that are removed by the hemoglobin in blood. These waste products travel in the blood to the lungs and are exhaled.

Cells use oxygen, together with glucose, as a source of energy to carry out a range of tasks. These tasks include muscle contraction, temperature maintenance, nerve conduction, and manufacturing new cells.

Remember these respiratory processes continue every minute of the day throughout your life. Unfortunately, human beings (supposedly the only life form with the ability to reason), persist in sabotaging this marvelous system. Some of you may start smoking, a habit that adds carbon dioxide to the air that you breathe. Imagine how well your car engine would run and how long it would last if you added carbon dioxide or smoke to its air intake.

Maintenance

1. Learn to breathe through your nose whenever possible. This warms the air before it enters the lungs. The nose also contains hairs and mucus that filters dust, pollen and bacteria from the air.

2. Don't smoke. By not smoking you dramatically reduce the risk of contracting heart disease, lung cancer or emphysema.

3. Exercise regularly to keep your lungs healthy and build up their capacity.

The Endocrine System

The endocrine system encompasses the pancreas, adrenal, pituitary, thyroid, parathyroid, ovaries and testes. These are some of the ductless glands in your body, and their purpose is to secrete hormones.

Hormones are chemical messengers that circulate through your blood.

Every system in your body is subject to the influence of hormones, either directly or indirectly. Your metabolism, water and mineral balance, growth, sexual development, and the ability to stimulate or inhibit nerve impulses can all be influenced by hormones.

Nerve impulses provide feedback to the brain. These impulses act like a thermostat to govern the flow of various hormones on demand.

The endocrine system is complex so it is prone to many disorders. The most common maladies are diabetes and thyroid problems.

Fortunately, because of medical advances, many of these disorders are controllable. Today most of the hormones in your body can be man made.

Maintenance

1. Any disorders of the endocrine system should be diagnosed and treated when they start.

2. Man-made hormones and other medications prescribed by a physician should be taken as directed. Serious problems often occur if medications are improperly taken.

3. Some disorders, such as diabetes, require a carefully controlled lifestyle.

The Digestive System

Your mouth, pharynx, esophagus, stomach, small intestine, large intestine and anus are the main parts of the digestive system. Teeth, salivary glands, liver, pancreas and gall bladder (with its associated bile ducts) are also parts of the digestive system.

When you eat, your teeth chew the food into small pieces and mix it with saliva that lubricates and partially digests the food. The tongue then pushes the food into the pharynx (a channel used for air and food).

The epiglottis is the flap or cartilage that seals the entrance to the larynx so the food enters the esophagus. Once food enters the esophagus, the epiglottis opens and allows you to breathe again.

Food moves through the esophagus into your stomach via involuntary flat muscles. Here it is mixed and churned with gastric and other digestive juices secreted by the stomach lining.

The partially processed food is gradually released into the small intestine where the liver, gall bladder and pancreas go to work. A digestive juice, called bile, is added by the liver and gall bladder. And the pancreas secretes more digestive juices that contain powerful enzymes.

In the small intestine the partially digested food is further broken down so nutrients can be absorbed and transferred into the blood and arteries. This absorption process is done by intestinal villi located in the walls of the small intestine.

The small intestine is about 15 or 16 feet long. As food moves through the small intestine most of the nutrients are absorbed before it enters the large intestine.

The large intestine is 4 or 5 feet long. It absorbs most of the water from digestive waste and changes it to feces that is excreted via the rectum and anus.

Once the food enters the pharynx the digestive process is automatic. However, you do have control over how you eat, what you eat, and when you excrete the feces.

You have to marvel at how the body monitors itself with such precision and continually feeds trillions of cells. Compare this with man's effort to feed the population of the world.

Maintenance

1. Eat slowly and chew well. This allows the saliva to start the digestive process.

2. Eat balanced meals with plenty of dietary fiber.

3. Exercise is good for healthy and regular bowel movements.

4. Eat poached, steamed or broiled foods. Avoid foods fried in fat.

5. Watch your fat intake. It takes about a mile of extra blood vessels to service an additional pound of fat.

6. Try not to eat junk food, or limit it to once in a while.

7. Brush and floss your teeth regularly.

The Immune System

The immune system is the body's security system. It guards the body from external germ invasions and protects it from internal malfunctions.

The white corpuscles, the main police force, grow in the bone marrow and lymph tissue.

There are five types of white blood cells that respond to specific germ invasions or cell malfunctions. These antibodies act as the body's surveillance system and look for germ invaders and abnormal cell divisions within tissues.

Once the immune system detects and overcomes germ invaders, it stores this information in a "memory bank." Then it can respond the same way if these germs are encountered again.

The body's immune system is often bolstered with vaccinations. For example, small pox is all but eradicated due to mass immunizations throughout the world.

Unfortunately, there are still many viruses or diseases that do not have any vaccines to prevent them, including AIDS and herpes.

Maintenance

1. Keep your immunizations and boosters for infectious diseases current.

2. Keep fit—don't let your body get run down.

3. Have regular medical examinations.

4. Eat a balanced diet.

5. Practice cleanliness. Germs are not attracted to clean surroundings.

6. Wash your hands thoroughly after each visit to the bathroom.

7. Do not drink from other people's cups or bottles.

8. Be sure the water you drink is safe.

9. Do not use illegal drugs.

The Urinary System

Your body is made up of 55 to 60 percent water. Different tissues contain various amounts of water.

Blood is about three times thicker than water, however about half of it is water.

The kidneys filter your blood, removing waste products and turning them into urine. Blood passes through the kidneys 350 to 400 times each day for filtering. Only a small amount of water from the blood turns into urine. The rest stays in the blood stream.

Only enough water is removed from the blood stream to keep the body's inner chemistry in balance.

Once urine forms in the kidneys, it is stored in the bladder. When the bladder is full, you are alerted to urinate and empty it.

Maintenance

1. Drink plenty of fluid daily to replace the water lost in urine, sweat, tears and breathing.

2. The urinary tract is susceptible to infection. Urinary infections can quickly spread to your kidneys or blood, so have them diagnosed as soon as possible.

The Reproductive System

Human beings, like other mammals, have one biological function. That is to reproduce and try to insure the survival and well-being of its offspring.

Although we take the birth of a baby for granted, the actual mechanics of this process are complex.

Males and females each produce a different half of the genetic material needed to produce another human. Females produce an egg cell and males produce a sperm cell.

The egg cell and the sperm cell each carry genetic information called chromosomes. When the egg and the sperm unite in the female body the chromosomes randomly group into 23 pairs. Each pair contains one chromosome from the egg cell and one from the sperm cell.

The fertilized egg cell, with this new genetic information, keeps dividing and subdividing into the many diverse cells that form a baby.

Just imagine this! One fertilized egg cell divides into hundreds of billions of distinct cells that, taken together, form a new human being.

Maintenance

1. Proper nutrition, a good exercise program, and a controlled lifestyle, are the best way to prevent reproductive system problems.

2. Cancer is the main disorder of the reproductive system in later life. Early detection of cancer and improved treatment methods have helped.

3. Experimenting with sexual intercourse may be an exciting thought, but the results can be devastating.

4. Some sexually transmitted diseases are curable with antibiotics, but AIDS and herpes are not.

Hearing

The hearing system is your built-in amplification and balance center. It encompasses the outer ear (the auricle), the auditory canal, the ear drum and the tiny bones in the middle ear—the hammer, anvil and stirrup.

Sound waves enter the outer ear, travel through the auditory canal to the eardrum, and then on to the tiny bones in the middle ear.

In the inner ear the sound vibrations stimulate the sensory organs. This stimulation sends electrical impulses along one of the cranial nerves to the brain for deciphering.

The inner ear contains a complex balancing mechanism. It is made up of three semi-circular canals (filled with a jelly-like fluid), vestibular nerves, special-ized cells, and sensory cells with fine hair attached. As the sound moves through the inner ear, it disturbs the jelly-like fluid in each canal. This disturbance alerts receptors that collect information. The combined information from the receptors provides the brain with a sense of three-dimensional movement so it can establish your place, position and orientation.

Maintenance

1. Exposure to excessive noise can cause irreversible damage to your ears. Keep the stereo turned down to a moderate volume.

2. Wear protective gear in a noisy work environment.

3. Protect your ears against the elements. They are particularly vulnerable to frost bite and sunburn.

4. If you have ear wax build-up, have a doctor remove it. Never put tissue in your ear to try and clean it. The tissue will only push the wax against the eardrum and possibly rupture it.

5. Never put anything smaller than your elbow in your ear. Now just try putting your elbow in your ear!

Sight

The sight system is another complex network that allows you to interact visually with your surroundings.

The main part of the sight is, of course, the eye. It comprises the cornea, pupil, iris, lens and retina.

The cornea, pupil, iris and lens work very much like a camera. The retina is more complex, it has millions of light sensitive cells that pass information to the brain via the optic nerve for deciphering.

If you have good eyes, you see everything in focus. This focusing process forms pictures that your brain stores for future use.

If you are near- or far-sighted you may need glasses to correct your vision. Fortunately, today's technology can correct most eye problems.

The color of your eyes is inherited from your parents' genes. The most common eye colors are blue and brown.

Maintenance

1. Get a reasonable amount of sleep every night so your eyes, as well as your body, are well rested.

2. If you wear glasses, buy shatter-proof lenses.

3. Wear safety glasses that are designed for proper eye protection. This is particularly important in a workshop setting or when playing racquet sports.

4. Use a good light source when reading, writing, or doing crafts.

5. Wear sunglasses that have the proper ultraviolet rating to protect your eyes.

6. When skiing or sailing in the sun, wear sunglasses that have side shields as well as ultraviolet ray protection.

7. If you get something in your eye, immediately flush it with water for several minutes. If this does not help see a doctor for attention.

Summary

This is a very condensed version about the amazing systems that make your body function. As you are growing up, take time to read some of the current books on the human body and family health. It will be an interesting experience and time well spent.

&

Kindness is a language everybody understands.

&

Laughter is a tranquilizer with no side effects.

&

No one is ever too old to learn, but most people keep putting it off.

&

You can save two things by driving slowly, gasoline and your life.

ॐ

*DEBT—When you set and bait your
own trap, then crawl into it.*

ॐ

*The most difficult arithmetic to master
is the art of counting your blessings.*

ॐ

*It is not what we read, but what we can
remember that makes us smart.*

ॐ

*The trouble with mornings,
they always come when I'm not awake.*

CHAPTER TWO

NUTRITION

How To Be Happy
If you want to be happy
Begin where you are
Don't wait for some rapture
that's future and far.
Begin to be joyous, begin
to be glad and soon you'll
forget that you ever were sad.

The Horizon

———

Money won't buy happiness, but it will pay the salaries of a large research staff to study the problem.

Bill Vaughan

———

Never forget the basic fact about yourself, you are greater and finer than you think you are.

Norman V. Peal

———

I am only one
But still I am one.
I cannot do everything.
But still I can do something;
And because I cannot do everything
I will not refuse to do the something
I can do.

Edward Everett Hale

———

One of the greatest sources of energy is pride in what you are doing.

Spokes

Probably all of us need to eat more sensibly. During youth, you usually don't buy or prepare the food you eat. However, as you grow older and start cooking and eating out you will be in control of your food intake. So it is a good idea to study and understand nutrition. This will help you to choose foods that are good for you.

The following is a simple guideline to good nutrition.

A Simple Guideline

- Eat a variety of foods.

- Maintain a healthy weight.

- Choose a diet low in fat, saturated fat and cholesterol.

- Choose a diet with plenty of vegetables, fruits and grain products.

- Use sugars in moderation.

- Use salt in moderation.

Good Food Choices

The Cancer Research Society of Canada suggests the following foods have good disease-fighting powers.

Vegetables

- Broccoli, brussels sprouts, cabbage and cauliflower. These provide insoluble fiber, beta carotene, Vitamin C, folate, calcium and iron.

- Romaine lettuce, endive, watercress, kale, spinach, chard and turnip greens provide beta carotene and Vitamin C.

- Potatoes contain carbohydrates, Vitamins C and B6, copper, magnesium, phosphorous, iron and fiber.

- Sweet pepper is an excellent source of Vitamin C.

- Carrots and sweet potatoes are good sources of beta carotene.

- Lima beans, navy beans, pinto beans, lentils, peas and kidney beans are also recommended.

Fruits

- Oranges, grapefruits, tangerines, pomegranates, persimmons, mangoes, apricots, cantaloupe and papaya are excellent sources of Vitamin C.

- Blueberries, strawberries, blackberries, raspberries, apples, bananas, pears and cherries are rich in fiber.

Grains

- Whole wheat, pasta, barley, wheat germ, brown rice or fiber-rich cereals like oatmeal are all good choices.

Miscellaneous

- Garlic, onions and leeks may help lower cholesterol.
- Canola oil and olive oil may aid in lowering total cholesterol and raise helpful HDL cholesterol.

Counting Calories

About one-third of the American population is overweight. To change the eating habits of the average adult is a tough chore. So educating the young on the benefits of following good nutritional guidelines may be more practical.

If you follow these guidelines and see the results —good health and a good figure—then perhaps you can persuade the adults in your household to do the same.

By law, most canned and pre-packaged foods require a nutrition facts panel. These panels could be a great help to the shopper. Unfortunately, by the time you see the food on the table, the panels are not there to help you.

A more efficient way, from your point of view, may be to buy a pocket calorie counter booklet. The booklet should give the calories, fat and cholesterol content for each serving of food. Also, it should include the "fast foods" you may wish to sample once in a while.

Ask your doctor what you should weigh. Then find out the number of calories you need daily to keep your body operating and provide enough energy for your lifestyle.

The daily calorie requirement is the amount of food necessary to carry on the daily routine of living, plus the amount needed for growth and maintenance of body tissues. The needs of individuals vary according to their size and activity level.

Usually your body requires about 10 calories daily for each pound you weigh. Remember your body always counts calories. Once consumed, there is no way to prevent the calories from going to work.

The amount of calories used, that are made up of fat, govern your weight. It is true your body needs some fat to function. However, it does not need a surplus of fat to store around your waist or thighs.

If you weigh more than is recommended for your size, you may need to go on a straight calorie and exercise diet. However, be sure to consult your doctor before you go on a stringent diet and exercise program.

For every pound you want to lose you will have to short change your body about 3,500 to 4,000 calories. Needless to say, it is a challenge to plan a balanced daily diet that still keeps your total calorie intake at the desired level.

The best way to solve a weight problem is not to have one. Some of you are lucky and have genes that let you eat anything you want and not gain a pound, but others are not so lucky and have to manage their diet carefully.

Countless studies continue to prove there is a significant relationship between your diet and the risk of developing life-threatening diseases or other health problems in the future.

It only takes a little knowledge and planning, and a whole lot of willpower to make a difference.

᠍

Sorrow looks back—Worry looks
ahead—Happiness is now.

Laughter is the shock absorber,
that eases the blows of life.

Don't take to crime because there are
so many legal ways to be dishonest.

To be without a friend is the same
as living in poverty.

If your problems are all behind you,
then you must be a school bus driver.

CHAPTER THREE

EXERCISE

Statistics
Facts mean nothing unless they are rightly understood, rightly rated and rightly interpreted.

R.L. Long

———

Preventing hardships–why is it that parents try so hard to keep their children from having the same hardships they had–that made them successful in life.

Hendry Fredrick

———

You cannot box a sunset
It is hard to wrap up snow
There is no way to
package a
lighted candle's
glow
Enjoy each lovely
moment
As you walk along
the way
There is a bit of beauty
in every passing day.

Joyce J. Johnson

———

Women have much more imagination than men. They need it to tell us how wonderful we are.

Arnold Glasow

A good exercise program is the best preventive medicine in the world. Even better, most of it is free, it requires very little learning, and it can be done in a variety of ways.

When exercising, it's a good idea to concentrate on using the large muscles in the legs and arms to burn excess fat. However, don't forget to exercise the rest of your muscles to keep them in tone.

Although we sometimes take health for granted, many studies show that exercise can perform magic for the body and mind.

Facts

Here are some interesting facts about exercise.

Exercise helps:

- prevent heart disease by increasing the efficiency of the heart.

- lower the resting heart rate.

- reduce blood pressure and strengthens the heart muscles.

- strengthen bones, muscles and body tissue.

- maintain your desired weight when combined with a sensible diet.

- increase the level of good cholesterol in your blood.

- control diabetes.

- your body use oxygen more effectively, giving you more stamina.

- improve your posture.

- you sleep better.

- you handle stress and fight off depression.

- you recover from an operation, broken bones or illness of any type.

Have you noticed that after a good workout, walk or jog, you feel better. Sometimes you may feel as if you are walking on air.

Getting involved in a good exercise program when you are young and continuing it through to adulthood is a winning combination to prevent and cure many illnesses.

Try to think of one medicine that can do so much for your body and mind. Unfortunately, despite all the proof about the benefits of exercise, statistics point to an increasingly sedentary nation.

Statistics

Some of the statistics about exercise are encouraging, others are not.

The proportion of Americans who exercise moderately (at least five times a week), increased from 22% in 1987 to 24% in 1991.

Recently, more people have been exercising regularly. Regular exercise is defined as performing any single fitness activity at least 100 times per year. Nearly 50 million people made this claim last year, up 11% from the previous year.

Health club memberships increased to more than 20 million.

Young adults are not helping the averages. The percentage of 18 to 24 year olds who engaged in sports dropped from 66% in 1982 to 59% in 1992. Between 1985 and 1990 alone, there was a 15% decline in exercise.

It appears many of us prefer watching sports at the stadium or on TV instead of actually participating. In spite of our higher education, statistics prove we are drifting more and more to a "push button" and sedentary lifestyle.

Now is the time to reverse this trend. Take advantage of what exercise can do for you when you are young.

ॐ

*Experience is great, it tells you when
you have made the same mistake again.*

ॐ

Children have more need of models than of critics.

ॐ

*You can't plan for the future in the future,
now is the time to do it.*

ॐ

*A big man will show you his bigness by the
way he treats the little people.*

CHAPTER FOUR

PREVENTION

Born Equal
Woman was created from the rib of man;
She was not made from his head to top him;
Nor from his feet to be tramped on.
But out of his side to be equal to him;
Under his arm to be protected by him;
And near his heart, to be loved by him.

Author Unknown

———

My life is in the hands of any fool who makes me lose
my temper.

Dr. John Hunter

———

Judge a woman not by her charms but her qualities;
judge a man not by his birth but his conduct; judge a
scholar not by his learning but by his achievement; and
judge a merchant not by his fortune but by his
understanding.

Hindu proverb

———

Praise makes good men better and bad men worse.

Thomas Fuller

———

Why is it when a guy has an accident he says, "it's
fate," but if he makes a hole in one he feels personally
responsible?

Michael Douglas

———

Nothing is lost until you begin to look for it.
Ruth Austin

The life expectancy of human beings in America is increasing. The reasons for the increase are greater knowledge of health problems, newer methods for treating injuries, and cures for various illnesses. The mortality rate at birth also has decreased.

You take it for granted, when you get sick or hurt, that the doctor will restore you to good health. However, if you look more closely, you will see that the increase in life expectancy was achieved more by prevention and good health promotion, rather than by treatment and curative measures.

Vaccines

Think of all the lives that were saved, and are still being saved, by the development of vaccines. Small pox, polio, hepatitis and typhoid are just a few examples. A simple shot in the arm when you are young can program your immune system to defend against these germs for years to come.

Discipline

Unfortunately, today's major killers, heart disease, cancer, strokes and AIDS cannot be prevented by a vaccine. However, to a large extent, they can be controlled by your lifestyle.

This lifestyle includes proper nutrition, a good exercise program, maintaining an ideal body weight, managing stress, avoiding smoking, excessive alcohol, illegal drugs and promiscuous sex.

Good Health Habits

To establish good health habits you need to understand your body and its needs. Use your doctor, dentist, parents and teachers as advisors and educators to help you gain this knowledge. It is fine to try for high grades in school, but you also need to budget time for your body.

As you get older it's harder to discipline yourself, and it's easy to slip into bad habits such as smoking. So try and establish good healthy habits while you are young.

Now, more than ever, you must take a greater share of the responsibility for your own well-being.

Protection From The Sun

Sun tanning, so popular with the young, should be handled with extreme care. Remember the sun can be your friend or your enemy.

Researchers predict that as many as 1 in 7 people born in America today will eventually develop some type of skin cancer.

An unprotected soak in the sun is a sure way to damage your skin. The dangers of sunburn are:

- Photo aging, a premature breakdown in the quality of the skin.

- Sun-induced skin cancers such as carcinoma, basal cell carcinoma, non-melanoma, and the most dangerous of all, malignant melanoma.

Sunburns are unforgiving. They are a signal that your skin system has been overwhelmed. A sunburn when you are young may come back and create problems later in life.

Sunburns are caused by ultraviolet rays. There are three types of ultraviolet rays, namely: UVAs, UVBs and UVCs.

UVAs penetrate the deepest layers of skin and can cause photo aging and skin cancers.

UVBs attack the surface of the skin. Your body tries to protect itself against UVB rays by increasing the production of a pigment called melanin. This production of melanin is what gives you a sun tan.

UVCs are filtered out by the ozone protection layer. However, as ozone layer is constantly being eroded by man, the risk of dangerous UVC penetration increases.

Sunscreens are available to offer partial protection against UV rays. They are rated by a SPF factor. A SPF factor of 6 will allow you to stay in the sun for 60 minutes before burning. A SPF factor of 8 allows you 80 minutes, and so on.

Keep in mind that you are not totally protected by most sunscreens because the SPF factor only protects against varying amounts of UVB rays. Supposedly, there are newer sunscreens on the market that create a total sun block. However, these products only claim to offer partial protection against UVA rays.

Before exposing your body to the sun, take time to seek expert advice on sun protection. Always remember that prevention is only useful before a problem arises, not after it exists.

Recent studies show that sufficient amounts of antioxidants (beta carotene, Vitamin C and Vitamin E) in your diet will help protect your skin.

☙

Laughter is the sun that drives
winter from the human face.

CHAPTER FIVE

SAFETY

Worry never robs tomorrow of its sorrows; it only saps today of its strength.

J. A. Aronin

———

Little Boy: How long is it until Christmas?
Mother: Oh, it's a long way off.
Little Boy: Let me know when it's time to start being good.

———

There is sufficiency in the world today for man's need but not for man's greed.

Mahandas K. Gandi

———

Every young man should learn to take criticism. He'll probably be a parent some day.

Franklin P. Jones

———

HE WHO TALKS LIKE A BIG WHEEL MAY ONLY BE A SPOKESMAN.

John Berryhill

———

The test of the heart is trouble, and it always comes with years; and the smile that is worth the praise of earth, is the smile that shines through tears.

Ella W. Wilcox

You ultimately bear the responsibility for keeping out of harm's way. You owe this to yourself, your family, peers, fellow students and co-workers.

It is not enough to get an education. You must, in the process, learn about safety and try to practice it in every phase of your life.

When you are young, you depend on parents and teachers to teach you about safety. As you grow older, however, you must expand your knowledge by studying and practicing safety rules in the home, school and on streets and highways.

Home Accidents

Every year, in America, 20,000 people die and about 2,000,000 require medical attention because of home accidents. Children and the elderly are the victims of most of these accidents.

These statistics should not be taken lightly. Most of the deaths and injuries are from falls, fires, poisoning, suffocation, drowning, firearms, burns and electrical shocks that could be prevented.

If your parents are a bit lax about safety in the home, maybe you should take it upon yourself to try to help correct this situation. Instead of buying your favorite magazine, buy a booklet on home safety—it could be a life saver.

Walking Tips

If you weren't taught all the rules about safe walking, or have forgotten some of them, here are a few tips that will serve you well.

- Always walk on the inside of the sidewalk. If you walk on the outside and happen to stumble, you could fall in front of a moving vehicle.

- Stop at all driveways, alleys and areas without curbs. Proceed only after checking carefully for moving traffic.

- Make "Stop, Look and Listen" a habit. Stop before stepping into the road. Look all ways. Listen for vehicles. Check to see that cars have stopped. If possible, make eye contact with the driver.

- Obey traffic signs. Then look both ways before you cross the street.

- At controlled intersections, do not step out into the street as soon as the lights turns green. Check first to make sure vehicles have come to a complete stop.

- Learn the meaning of red, yellow and green lights and "Walk" and "Don't Walk" signs. Do not try to cheat on a yellow light or "Don't Walk" sign.

- At uncontrolled intersections learn to be extra alert. Follow the rules, without exception, and pay special attention to drivers.

- Railway crossings often cause problems. People ignore cross bars or think they can beat a speeding train. Many are killed. Some children think it's adventurous to walk along railway tracks or cross tracks at unmarked areas. Both habits are not only dangerous—they are illegal.

- When you are walking along rural roads, walk beside the road in single file, facing the traffic. If you have to walk on the road, stay as close to the edge as possible. (We think because we see a car coming they see us too. In fact, drivers do not expect to see pedestrians on rural roads).

It is unfair and dangerous to expect drivers to take all the responsibility for pedestrian safety. Remember you only have one life. Do not put it in the hands of others, even if you do have the right-of-way.

Cycling Tips

In America, nearly 30 to 40 million people cycle regularly for recreation. Another million or so use a bicycle to commute. Although federal legislation is encouraging local communities to build cycling paths, often it is difficult to change streets and bridges to make bicycle commuting safe.

There are 800 to 1,000 deaths and 40,000 accidents every year because of bicycle/automobile collisions. Nonetheless, people of all ages are riding bicycles with no special training and testing. Often they have no idea of their obligations and responsibilities as a cyclist.

Bikes are selling like "hotcakes" and bicycle accidents are escalating almost as fast as sales. One reason is people are purchasing bikes for children who are not ready for them. However, the main reason is there are not enough bicycle paths for children and adults to learn to ride safely before venturing out on busy streets.

There is a lot to learn about bicycle safety. If you have to use the same streets as the automobiles, here are some basic rules to follow:

- Always wear a helmet. Be sure it fits properly and is a bright color.

- Wear bright colored, reflective clothing. It is good for cycling any hour of the day.

- Use reflective tape on the pedals, spokes and rear reflectors.

- Install a light if you cycle at night.

- All bikes should have a horn or bell, and a proper chain guard.

- Have a proper basket installed for carrying books or parcels.

- Purchase your bike from a knowledgeable sales-person who will equip it according to your size and ability. Learn to adjust the handlebars, saddle, brakes and gears.

- Do not operate a taxi service by squiring others on the handlebars, seat or back fender.

- Don't wear headphones.

- Don't ride side by side when cycling.

- Get a booklet on safe cycling and a booklet from the Highway Traffic Board on the rules and laws governing traffic vehicles. Once your bicycle is in traffic area it is subject to the same rules as motor vehicles.

- If you are a new cyclist see if there is a bicycle training center in your city and go there to learn to ride.

- Use hand signals to alert other drivers of your intentions.

- When you cross railroad tracks, try to do so at right angles to the track or walk your bike across the tracks.

- Bike licenses are required by law in some areas. Other areas may have bicycle codes you must follow.

Motorcycle Facts

If you are thinking about buying a motorcycle, consider these statistics from the National Safety Council Accident Facts (1995 edition).

The number of registered motorcycles in the US totalled about 3,932,000. In 1994 motorcycles travelled an estimated 10.2 billion miles. The death rate was estimated at 25 motorcycle riders per every 100,000,000 miles travelled. This mortality rate is about 17 times higher than the rate for occupants of other types of vehicles.

These statistics show motorcycles are considerably more dangerous than other modes of transportation. This is because of their size and speed capability, combined with the fact they are not equipped with seat belts or exterior protection to cushion collisions.

Auto Safety

Usually when you reach the age when you can get a driver's license you are eager to start driving. Be sure you prepare well for this step.

After writing tests in school, it is simple enough to study the laws and rules of the road and pass the written exam. However, to learn, remember and apply these rules when you get behind the wheel takes some practice.

How do you parallel park? How much distance does it take to stop a car at various speeds and road conditions? What do you do if the car goes into a skid? Who has the right-of-way at unmarked intersections?

In some European countries, one or two months of schooling and training is required before issuing a license. Also, to qualify for a license you must be 18 years old. In this country, however, the laws are not so stringent.

It would be a wise decision to take driving training from a qualified individual or school and spend some time learning the rules of "defensive driving." Some cities have schools that teach driving on icy and muddy roads to teach you how to come out of a skid.

Even then you need PRACTICE, PRACTICE, PRACTICE to learn to control the vehicle and be aware of your surroundings. For your own safety, and others, be well prepared before you take to the road.

Swimming

Learn to swim when you are young. It's a great recreational sport that is good for your health and safety.

First Aid

Take a first aid course as soon as you are old enough and keep your certificate current. This is very helpful if you come upon an accident or plan to have a family of your own.

Safety Statistics

Here are some interesting statistics from the National Safety Council Accident Facts (1995 edition).

- In 1994 the Cost of Unintentional Injuries in the US was $440.9 billion, broken down as follows:
  - ◆ Motor Vehicle Damage–$39.1 billion.
  - ◆ Medical Expenses–$77.8 billion.
  - ◆ Fire Losses–$8.2 billion.
  - ◆ Employer Costs–$18.7 billion.
  - ◆ Administrative Expenses–$70.1 billion.
  - ◆ Wage & Productivity Losses–$227.0 billion.

The cost of unintentional injuries is immense. Figures in the billions are difficult to comprehend. So they have been converted to everyday amounts that are easier to understand.

The following statistics show how the 1994 cost of unintentional injuries compared to taxes, new car prices, stock dividends, etc.

- The cost of all injuries ($440.9 billion) was equivalent to 80 cents of every dollar paid in Federal personal income tax, or 65 cents of every food dollar spent in the US.

- Motor vehicle injuries cost ($176.5 billion) was equivalent to purchasing 800 gallons of gasoline per vehicle registered in the US, or a $19,100 rebate on each new car sold.

- Home injuries cost ($94.3 billion) was equivalent to 49 cents of every dollar of property taxes paid, or a $78,700 rebate on each new single family home built.

- Public injuries cost ($63.2 billion) was equivalent to a $7.0 million grant to every US public library, or a $86,900 bonus for each police officer or fire fighter.

- Work injuries cost ($120.7 billion) was equivalent to 59 cents of every dollar paid in corporate dividends to stockholders, or 23 cents of every dollar of pre-tax corporate profits.

The deaths cause by unintentional injuries in 1994 are listed below. Rates are per 100,000 population.

- All unintentional deaths–92,200. *Rate 35.4* broken down as follows:
  - ◆ Motor vehicle accidents–43,000 deaths (passenger automobiles–21,414). *Rate 16.5*.
  - ◆ Falls–13,300 deaths. *Rate 5.1*.

- ◆ Poisoning by solids and liquids–8,000 deaths. *Rate 3.1.*
- ◆ Fires, burns and deaths associated with fires–4,200 deaths. *Rate 1.6.*
- ◆ Drowning–4,000 deaths. *Rate 1.5.*
- ◆ Firearms (unintentional)–1,500 deaths. *Rate 0.6.*
- ◆ Poisoning by gas and vapors–700 deaths. *Rate 0.3.*
- ◆ All other types–14,500. *Rate 5.6.* This includes medical complications, misadventures, machinery, air transport, mechanical suffocation and excessive cold.

- • Passenger deaths per 100,000,000 miles travelled in 1993 were:
  - ◆ Automobiles–21,414. *Rate 0.82.*
  - ◆ Railroad–58. *Rate 0.42.*
  - ◆ Buses–14. *Rate 0.01.*
  - ◆ Airlines (scheduled)–19. *Rate 0.01.*

Unintentional deaths are the same whether they occur one at a time in a car accident, or 100 at a time in a plane crash. There is the same grief, sorrow and hardship to loved ones.

Unfortunately, more attention seems to be paid to aircraft safety than to all other types of unintentional deaths. This is upsetting when you compare the number of people who die in all types of accidents to those who die in planes.

Compare the following death rates to a aircraft carrying 450 passengers:

- 92,200 unintentional deaths equates to 205 planes crashing with no survivors.
- 43,000 motor vehicle deaths equates to 96 planes crashing with no survivors.
- 21,414 automobile passenger deaths equates to 48 planes crashing with no survivors, etc.

Some accidents are unavoidable, but think how many could be prevented by proper education alone. If safety was a mandatory subject in school, surely you would notice an enormous decline in the number of accidents and their cost in lives and money. If the 440 billion dollar yearly cost of accidents could be reduced, imagine the positive affect it would have on the country.

Many of you will become community leaders when you get older. Hopefully, you will have the wisdom to realize the terrible waste accidents cause and find ways to improve the record.

&

All in favor of conserving gasoline,
please raise your right foot.

*Education is the only thing that you
should get on the installment plan.*

*Worry is like a rocking chair, it gives you
something to do—but it doesn't get you anywhere.*

*A father is a man who expects his son
to be as good as he meant to be.*

*The most undeveloped territory in the country
lies under one's hat.*

CHAPTER SIX

MENTAL HEALTH

You have not lived today until you have done something for someone who can never repay you.
                                                    John Bunyan

___

Opportunity Awaits
With doubt and dismay you are smitten
You think there is no chance for you?
Why the best books haven't been written,
The best race hasn't been run,
The best score hasn't been made yet,
The best song hasn't been sung,
The best tune hasn't been played yet;
Cheer up, for the world is young!

No chance? Why, the world is just eager
For things that you ought to create
Its store of true wealth is still meager,
Its needs are incessant and great;
Don't worry and fret, faint hearted,
The chances have just begun
For the best jobs haven't been started,
The best work hasn't been done.

                                        Benton Braley

___

A FANATIC – is one who can't change his mind and won't change the subject.

                                        Churchill

___

The measure of a mans real character is what he would do if he knew he would never be found out.
                                        Thomas Macaulay

Good mental health is hard to define. It definitely includes balancing activities, practicing good health habits, and programming your mind to have a positive attitude.

You all know that from infancy to adulthood you pass through predictable stages of life. Each stage requires adjustments to cope with these changes. Knowing these stages occur and realizing your problems are not unique is a relief. Some of the problems associated with growing up were recognized in ancient times.

During youth it's the responsibility of your parents and teachers to recognize any mental health problems you may have. The teenage years, however, can sometimes be difficult. Therefore, if you know what to expect, you may appreciate your parents' efforts and be more cooperative.

There are several good family health books that have pages and pages of information on teenage mental health. Take time to read and study them. Even if you don't have any serious mental health concerns, this information will help you better understand a friend who may be having problems.

In any six month period, 1 in every 5 Americans has some form of mental health problem or illness. Despite this high percentage, there is still a "stigma" attached to mental illness. It seems it is more acceptable to have a physical ailment than to be depressed, the most common mental problem. Eventually, maybe this attitude will change and people with mental health problems will be treated equally.

Living A Balanced Life

Living a balanced life is paramount to your mental health. This involves balancing your daily activities—work, play and relaxation. Then realizing that sometimes you will need to adjust these activities to cope with everyday problems.

Laughter

Laughter is the "Best Medicine in the World." When you were a child you laughed and smiled all the time. Unfortunately, as you grow older, you use this wonderful medicine less and less.

A good laugh and a sincere smile are free. If you train yourself to have a good sense of humor, you will realize there is a lot to smile and laugh about. Think about a pretty bird singing, or a plant turning into a beautiful flower. Surely these thoughts should draw a smile or two.

Depression

Learn to be positive about life. Always count your blessings. Usually the problems you encounter that appear so unrelenting, will vanish after a good night's sleep. If they don't disappear then, they often will when you discuss them with someone you trust and respect.

Sometimes, however, you may need help from your parents or a family physician to solve problems. If you have a problem that is constantly weighing you down, get help from your parents or a health care professional.

Tragically more than 5,000 teenagers and young adults committed suicide this year and another 500,000 tried to. Suicide is the third leading cause of death among teenagers and the trend is increasing.

Constant depression can lead to suicide or suicide attempts. Because depression is so common today, it is important to know what it is so you can separate it from natural emotions. What causes depression? What can you do to prevent it? What are the signs you should watch for? If you know about depression, you can recognize it and do something.

Here are some suggestions to help prevent depression:

- Learn and practice good physical and mental health habits.

- Exercise regularly and get involved in sports.

- Stay away from illegal drugs and alcohol.

- Try to learn discipline and develop strong willpower. Be a leader, not a follower.

Treasure your life, it's a wonderful gift.

&

You can't give away kindness,
it keeps coming back.

&

The trouble with being a good sport,
is that you have to lose to prove it.

&

Things will come to you, if you
hustle while you wait.

CHAPTER SEVEN

CHARACTER

Sorry - NO TRADE IN
It is essential to learn and practice habits and attitudes
that will keep us healthy and strong, both physically
and mentally. Our parents and teachers try hard to
emphasize the need for these good attributes.
However, when we are young, we often take health
and life for granted. But as we get older and develop
serious problems, we then realize that WE CANNOT
TRADE OUR BODIES IN FOR NEW ONES.

Marvin and Joyce Sawyer

———

Experience -
is not what
happens to you -
it is what you do
with what happens
to you.

Aldous Huxley

———

I'm not afraid of the flying – I'm afraid of the
crashing.

D. Galyean

———

Poor and content is Rich and Rich enough.

Shakespeare

———

Think only of your self and your own needs and others
will soon forget you.

Dorothy Galyean

———

Good character building is as important as learning to read and write. Yet most schools do not offer a course on the subject.

You have to depend on example to help you mold your character. The examples include your parents, the TV you watch, the books and magazines you read, the friends you associate with, the movies you to go to, the church you attend, and the Internet you use.

You've probably heard or read about the good old days! Houses were never locked. Earning a living took up most of the spare time. Family life and values were important. Chaperons accompanied young girls to social occasions. Deals were struck and sealed with a handshake. People did not sue each other at the drop of a hat. And truth and honor were important. Problems with crime, illegal drugs, illegitimate children and failing marriages did not exist.

Life changed! Today most people live in towns or cities and depend on jobs that keep changing or disappearing. Many parents are without a job, or work for minimum wages.

You hear talk about family values, but is it a reality for all families? Because of divorce, separation, desertion and single-parent families, only about two-thirds of all American children live with both of their paternal parents.

All parents, divorced, single or otherwise, want their child to have a good, solid character. Perhaps a course in character building, acceptable to all nationalities and religions, would be useful in the education system. Well-planned children's TV programs and Internet information could also be a help.

Your character is part of the brain's "software." The software in your brain is programmed by what you see, hear and remember. It is to your advantage to program it properly.

Trust, Honesty and Integrity

As you study the various sciences and mathematics in school, you will come to the conclusion that they are based on truth and trust. You can trust the answer to the most complicated, or simple, mathematical problem. For example, you know that $10 + 10 = 20$ will remain constant and cannot be $10 + 10 = 21$.

The same applies to other sciences and most of the natural functions in our universe. We trust that there will be a sunrise and sunset, a day and a night, summers and winters, and so on.

Remember trust always follows truth and integrity. If you are caught cheating on an exam or lying to your parents, teachers, or anyone else, you will lose their trust and it will be very hard to regain. Furthermore, if you cheat on your body maintenance, nutrition and safety habits, you are not fooling anyone except yourself.

Honesty and integrity should not be compromised.

Love

Love is an emotion that comes in many forms. There is the love and respect for your parents, brothers and sisters, love of another person, love of your neighbors, love of your studies or job, love of nature, love of places, and love of your country.

It is also important to love yourself. It helps you live a healthy, balanced life so you can overcome problems and personal failures, and keep your self-esteem.

Love can be very beautiful, positive and sometimes powerful. Remember, careful cultivating will make it last and last.

Often you hear about another type of love that sometimes is not so wonderful. This is the love for material possessions. A few years ago enjoying life was simple, but as the standard of living improved, a passion for "toys" developed. These include CDs, tapes, bikes and an array of gadgets that are more elaborate and costly every year. This type of love is acceptable in moderation.

Manners

Good manners means you know how to behave properly in all situations. Many of you are taught good manners during your youth and at school, but you forget to use them.

Basic good manners are simple. It is easy to say, "Please" and "Thank You" and be courteous and act like a lady or gentleman.

Good manners are important. They reflect on your character throughout your life.

Tidiness

Tidiness is getting into the habit of keeping your surroundings clean, neat and in proper order.

Tidiness has to be learned and it takes practice. You learn to make your bed. You learn to hang up your clothes and keep your room clean. You learn to help keep the house, garage and yard clean. You learn to keep your school assignments clear and neat.

If you practice tidiness in everything you do, it makes you feel good and pays dividends for the rest of your life.

Cheerfulness

Fortunate are those who are always cheerful. These people usually do not realize it, but a good sense of humor and a cheerful disposition is often worth more than wealth. In fact, cheerfulness is an emotion seldom found in the wealthy.

Try to save some of the laughter and smiles you had as a baby. Don't let them disappear when you grow older. Some of us are lucky to have family and friends that set a good precedent. These are the parents who still smile though their day was awful, or the friend who boosts your spirits in spite of their own setbacks.

All of us are not so fortunate! However, that does not mean that you should give up trying to have a cheerful disposition. You may not like your appearance, or be on the Dean's honor roll, or be the star football player or cheerleader, but you must realize there is much to be thankful for. Life can be wonderful if you let it.

Willpower

Willpower means controlling your actions and emotions.

Strong willpower can be described as an enigma that drives you. It might be learning to follow good health habits, safety habits and a good exercise program. Or it could be staying in school until you get a good education, learn the laws of your country, or learn to be cheerful, tidy, well mannered, patient, kind, faithful and honest.

A strong willpower keeps you from doing things that are not so good, like smoking, drinking to excess, using illegal drugs, cheating, stealing, quarreling, gossiping, fighting and breaking the law.

Willpower and self-control is harder for adults to achieve. For example, heart attacks are the leading cause of death in the US. Most adults know that half an hour of proper exercise every second day will improve their chance of survival. However, it takes willpower to do this. Statistics show that only 1 in 10 adults take the time to follow this advice.

Strong willpower is strength and you need it if you want to live a long, healthy and successful life.

Patience

Patience is the capacity to put up with hard work, pain, trouble and adversity with the hope of attaining some level of accomplishment.

When you listen to an orchestra playing, do you realize how much time, work and patience the musicians spend to become so accomplished? Or, you may have watched your mother feeding your baby brother, trying to satisfy his whims and keep him from crying. Think about the patience a mother needs to raise a child from infancy to adulthood?

We all take a lot for granted. However, to learn a trade, a profession, or have the possessions you dream of, all takes time, hard work and patience.

Many of us are impatient about little things. For instance, we find delays of any kind unacceptable. Or we become irritated and demanding if we do not get what we want, when we want it. It is a sign of wisdom when you learn to accept delays graciously, maybe even with a smile.

Freedom

Man has exhibited a deep-rooted love for freedom from the beginning of time. The world's annals are full of the struggles of people striving to achieve freedom.

Freedom in America can be defined as the right of individuals, living in a social community under an elected government, to act as they choose, subject to the restraints imposed by law.

Total, unrestricted freedom of actions would make life impossible. The idea of people having the right to act, without restraints, if their actions do not interfere or violate the rights of others, may sound great in theory. However, in practice it would a disaster.

Our freedom in this country should be cherished. If you break the law and end up in jail you realize what you've lost. Likewise, when you travel to another country that does not have the same freedom, you realize how lucky you are.

Freedom is sometimes a double-edged sword. The First Amendment gives us many rights, including the right to march in peaceful protest rallies. Be sure to use good judgment of the present and future ramifications before you get too involved.

As time passes, more freedom is gained. However, some of this freedom (sexual promiscuity, pornography and gambling), may not be appropriate. Many legislators feel these activities are not the proper ingredients for a stable life.

It takes strength, wisdom, willpower and help from parents and teachers to avoid freedom that may cause you sorrow in the future.

Kindness

A dictionary may define kindness as helpful, friendly, sympathetic, thoughtful and gentle.

How do you attain these virtues? Well, you learn them just like you learned to walk, eat, study and work hard.

To learn kindness by example helps, but practice is the best way. By bestowing kindness on your family, friends, peers and the underprivileged you attain this virtue.

There is a genuine need for kindness in your interpersonal relationships. Needless quarrels, squabbles and fighting are avoided when you reach out in kindness, instead of anger. This applies to everyday life, as well as to the needless strife that constantly plagues the world.

True kindness means helping others without expecting anything in return.

Responsibility

As you grow up, you learn how to walk, eat, converse, behave, and look after your body. You also learn to work, obey the laws of your country, and to differentiate between right and wrong.

Although you rely on others, you must realize that you alone are responsible for your overall care and relationships with others. Keep a watchful eye and a firm hand on your appetites, passions, desires and actions. Make these cravings your servant, not your master.

Responsibility is the ability to turn knowledge and wisdom into positive, reliable day-to-day practices. To resist and overcome temptation is a sign in the right direction.

The Code of Life

> *Do Unto Others*
> *As You Would Have Others Do Unto You.*

Simple, only a few words! This code or "golden rule" is not new—it's been around for centuries. Unfortunately, only a few people take it seriously, practice it, and realize how important it is.

If all genders, nationalities, religions and colors were taught and practiced this code in every phase of their lives, what a different world it would be! There would be no wars, murders, racism, stealing and lying. In turn, there would be less poverty, and maybe, only a very few marriage failures.

To live by the "golden rule" takes time, hard work, cooperation and a strong will to make things better for everyone.

Think about it for a minute. Wouldn't it be worth it to live by this code.

Marriage Preparation

What is marriage? A dictionary or encyclopedia may define it as a social institution involving the union of men and women, in a form of mutual dependence, to create and maintain families.

Marriage is entered into through a contractual ceremony. It is often considered the most important contract a human being makes. If this is true, why aren't we preparing for marriage so it will last?

We have a plethora of knowledge on what makes marriages work and what makes marriages end up in divorce. However, we keep making the same mistakes over and over. How often do you hear, "Before the marriage he kissed the ground she walked on. One month later, they were screaming at each other."

Does your school or home prepare you for a successful marriage, or should you, as an individual, also contribute? As young children you read stories that had an ending like, "they got married and lived happily every after." This does not seem to be true in most marriages, but it could be.

You do not become a doctor, architect, engineer, nurse, accountant or any other professional unless you take time to prepare. For a marriage to run smoothly and last, a husband and wife need to spend time during their youth preparing for this step.

There is so much information available on what causes marriages to fail and what ingredients are needed to make it last. Surely, we can learn from the mistakes of others.

Remember that love, happiness and marriage should go together. You have the choice of making marriage the most beautiful thing on earth, or making it "hell" on earth.

-

A mother's patience is like a tube of
toothpaste, it's never quite all used up.

-

Mighty Futuristic Weapon - "TRUTH"
Today: *There is a new telephone equipped with sophisticated computer chips that will warn you if the incoming voice that you hear is not truthful. According to reports, this device is quite accurate.*
Near Future: *Badly needed a similar, foolproof computer device which if connected to an average home TV set would warn viewers whenever falsehoods appeared on its screen.*
However, if your communications with each other had to be **TRUTHFUL,** *how simple real justice, crime control and lasting peace could become. A challenge for you, the future leaders of our planet.*

CHAPTER EIGHT

ENVIRONMENT

If money is your only hope of independence, you will never have it. The only real security that man can have in this world is a reserve of knowledge, experience and ability.

Henry Ford

I'll say one thing for the good old days: cars couldn't stop on a dime but they could run on one.

Robert Orben

I STILL THINK THE HIGHWAYS WOULD BE SAFER IF WE LEFT THE CARS ALONE AND INSPECTED THE DRIVERS EVERY YEAR.

Dan Valentine

To be content, look backward on those who possess less than yourself, not forward on those who possess more. If this does not make you content, you don't deserve to be happy.

Benjamin Franklin

Understanding Your Body
Your body can be fully understood only by knowing what happens at the three levels of organs, cells and molecules. For instance, the movements of your eyes as they scan this line of text can be understood as the coordinated contractions of the set of six muscles (organs) that move each eye, as the actions of the specialized muscle cells from which those muscles are built, or as the interactions of proteins actin and myosin (molecules) in the muscle cells which enable them to contract.

Dr. Philip Whitfield

You probably remember from your science classes in school, Earth is part of the solar system. The solar system consists of the sun, its nine planets and multiple asteroids, comets and meteors.

The planets, in order of their distance from the sun, are Mercury, Venus, Earth, Mars, Jupiter, Saturn, Uranus, Neptune and Pluto.

The Planet Earth

Since we all live on Earth, let's review some of its features:

- It is the fifth largest of the nine planets.

- Earth is approximately 93,000,000 miles from the sun.

- Its circumference at the equator is approximately 25,000 miles.

- Its diameter at the equator is approximately 7,900 miles.

- The total area of the Earth's surface is approximately 197 million square miles.

- Earth rotates on its axis once every 23 hours, 56 minutes and 4.1 seconds (day).

- Earth and its satellite moon move together in an elliptical orbit around the sun at a speed of 66,000 MPH once every 365.2425 days (year).

- Earth has four parts: the atmosphere, the lithosphere, the hydrosphere and the centrosphere.

The Atmosphere

The atmosphere (air) is the gaseous envelope that surrounds our planet. At sea level, dry air is made up of 78 percent nitrogen, 21 percent oxygen and small quantities of carbon dioxide, ozone and inert gases. Air rises up to 300 miles, becoming thinner and lighter as it ascends.

Air makes our planet habitable. Oxygen sustains life. Carbon dioxide is absorbed by the trees and helps regulate the planet's temperature through the greenhouse effect. A layer of ozone protects life from the damaging ultraviolet radiation of the sun.

The Land (Lithosphere)

The lithosphere is the solid crust of the Earth. This layer is about 20 to 25 miles deep. It contains the soil used for growing food, the minerals for mining, and the channels for rivers and other bodies of water.

The Water (Hydrosphere)

Water covers more than 70 percent of the Earth's surface. This includes the oceans, inland seas, lakes, rivers, streams and underground water. The average depth of an ocean is about 12,500 feet.

Water is a composed of two gaseous elements— oxygen and hydrogen. Pure water freezes at 0°C (Centigrade) with a slight expansion, and boils at 100°C, giving off steam.

The Centrosphere

The centrosphere is below the crust of the Earth and makes up more than 99 percent of the Earth's mass.

A large part of the centrosphere is molten, or extremely hot. This is what you see when a volcano erupts and lava spills over.

Deforestation

Global deforestation is raising awareness of how important trees are for the health of our planet.

Green plants and trees undergo normal respiration, On average, they absorb five times as much carbon dioxide in photosynthesis as they expel in respiration. In turn, they release five times as much oxygen as they consume.

Carbon dioxide comes from industrial activity and automobile exhaust. By removing carbon dioxide from the air, plants and trees help balance the greenhouse effect of global warming. In turn, they provide us with clean, oxygen-filled air to breathe.

The effect of deforestation is upsetting this balance. Many countries allow massive logging operations in forests, including the rain forests. Today, rain forests are cleared at the rate of about 50 acres per minute.

If this practice continues, it will interfere with the delicate balance of our weather systems that create global temperatures and regional rain.

In some areas that are logged, trees are being replanted. However, man is taking out more than he is putting back.

There are, of course, forest fires caused by lightening and accidents. Fortunately, these fires can usually be controlled by firefighters and the destroyed trees gradually replanted.

It is important to realize that we share the space on this Earth with other animals and birds. If their natural habitat is destroyed, so is the balance of nature.

Water Pollution

Water pollution is a major problem. It is caused by oil spills, dumping industrial waste, and raw sewage into bodies of water.

The major oil spills, caused by ocean tankers running aground, are man-made accidents. But like all accidents, many could be avoided. Thankfully, the dumping of industrial waste and raw sewage is being monitored and discontinued in many places.

Wars always take a heavy toll on the environment. Cities and countrysides are bombed and burned. The Persian Gulf War is a prime example of water pollution. Seven hundred oil wells were set ablaze and a large amount of oil was released into the Persian Gulf.

Many of these disasters are cleaned up as quickly as possible, but new ones keep occurring in our oceans, lakes and rivers. Controlling water pollution is expensive, but very necessary.

If our civilization is to survive, fresh water is a necessity.

Air Pollution

The air is polluted by both nature and mankind. Forest fires, caused by lightening, pollute the air by discharging smoke and other gases. Active volcanoes blast unlimited gases, including sulfur dioxide, into the atmosphere and stratosphere.

Mankind pollutes the air by burning fossil fuels in factories and automobiles. In some places the smoke and gases released from industrial operations and power-generating plants cause "acid rain." When this falls to the ground as rain or snow, it kills forests, destroys life in lakes and rivers, and causes health problems for humans.

Nature is responsible for acid rain and some other types of pollution. However, nature's contribution to the air pollution problem is minuscule compared to that of man.

The cost of eliminating acid rain and other forms of air pollution is expensive, but the damage to the plant and animal kingdoms is beyond any dollar value.

Recycling

Disposing of garbage is an ever-growing problem as the world's population increases. It many areas, garbage is taken to a selected area and dumped. Some of the garbage is set afire, but the rest builds-up and soon another disposal site is required.

Many cities are recycling. Newspapers, bottles and cans are collected and the raw materials in them are reused. Old cars are compressed and melted down. The waste food from hotels and restaurants is being collected, cooked and fed to pigs.

We need to recycle. Many of the raw materials used to make everyday items are not renewable and will not be attainable for future generations.

Conservation

Conservation is the wise use of all natural resources. There are two types of natural resources: renewable and non-renewable.

Renewable resources include forests, foliage plants of all kinds, wildlife and soil.

Non-renewable resources are those that cannot be replaced once they are used. They include fossil fuels, coal, petroleum, natural gas, metallic and other ores.

Mankind has been aware of the need for conservation since ancient times. Unfortunately, this awareness has not prevented some disastrous results. Generally, the basic principles of land use have been ignored throughout the world. Centuries of uncontrolled livestock grazing has created large, barren areas in Africa, the Near East, and in many newer developed regions of the world.

The pioneers destroyed forest and grassland areas to cultivate the land. This caused erosion. The Earth's rich topsoil disappeared in floods and dust storms. Your grandparents probably remember the drought and dust storms of the 1930s and the tremendous loss of topsoil.

Today, many companies are in business to gain maximum yields from the forest industry. The history of forest lands in North America illustrates the progression of this ruthless exploitation.

Fortunately, some countries realize that resources are not unlimited and have legislated better forest and land management.

Regrettably, the US leads the world in per capita consumption of non-renewable resources, but the trend is worldwide. On a brighter side, the efficiency of extraction and utilization has improved and advances in technology are continually revealing new sources of non-renewable resources.

When the settlers arrived there were large populations of animals, birds and fish. Settlement brought the heavy, and sometimes senseless, slaughter of the most abundant and desirable species. Cultivation, fire, pollution, drainage and over-grazing destroyed large areas of suitable habitat for many animals. The result was a drastic decrease in all forms of wildlife.

Through the years, measures have been adopted to preserve wildlife. International cooperation and agreement has been reached to regulate commercial fishing, establish game reserves, control stream pollution, stabilize water levels, and restore forests and rangeland. Recently, some organizations have even been formed to monitor wildlife abuse.

Maintaining the balance of nature is paramount. History proves all living things were created for a reason, and that we must learn to share and preserve the environment.

⌗

*Please, ask not what your country can do
for you—but what it can do for me.*

⌗

*Use what little talent that you have.
It would be a shame if only the birds that sang
best would sing.*

---

*No one ever ruined his eyesight by looking
at the brighter side of life.*

*Knowledge is a treasure chest.
Practice is the key to it.*

*The worst thing about history, is that every
time it repeats itself, the price goes up.*

*I have yet to be bored when someone
is paying me a compliment.*

CHAPTER NINE

TODAY'S PROBLEMS

A True Home

A house without love may be a castle or a palace but it is not a home; love is the life of a true home. A home without love is no more a home than a body without a soul is a man.

John Lubbock

————

Help Yourself to Happiness

Everybody, everywhere
*   seeks happiness, it's true,*
But finding it and keeping it
*   Seems difficult to do.*
Difficult because we think
*   - that happiness is found*
Only in places where
*   wealth and fame abound –*
And so we go on searching
*   in "palaces of pleasure"*
Seeking recognition
*   and monetary treasure,*
Unaware that happiness
*   is just a "state of mind"*
Within the reach of everyone
*   who takes time to be kind –*
For in making OTHERS HAPPY
*   we will be happy, too.*
For the happiness you give away
*   returns to "shine on you."*

Helen Steiner Rice

————

Worry grows lushly in the soil of indecision.

Ben Turnbull

Drugs

Drugs come from plant, mineral, and animal products, or they are made synthetically. There are prescription drugs and illegal street drugs.

Prescription drugs are manufactured by large pharmaceutical companies and go through stringent testing before they are approved. They are prescribed by a doctor who must give explicit instructions on their use. They also must list common side effects and the procedures to follow if an overdose is taken. Prescription drugs are usually taken to cure or prevent a disease, control a mental problem, or ease discomfort and pain.

Some prescription drugs are addictive and habit-forming. It takes strength and willpower to stop using them when they are no longer needed.

Illegal street drugs are manufactured by a small firm or chemist. They are not tested and their contents are not listed. No instructions are provided for overdoses or possible side effects. These drugs are sold illegally, usually on the street. They are used to give people a temporary "high" (a sense of euphoria). Illegal drugs are extremely addictive and can have devastating side effects.

The common illegal drugs are marijuana, hashish, cocaine, crack, LSD and Angel Dust. Short-term use of milder drugs often leads to experimenting with more potent drugs and eventual addiction.

Some authorities consider alcohol, tobacco and the caffeine in coffee and tea as habit-forming drugs. Except for tobacco, these drugs are reasonably safe, if used in moderation. Cola pops also contain caffeine.

It would be a worthwhile experience for all young people to visit a drug and alcohol treatment centre. Then they could see the terrible ordeal and pain that addicts go through because of drug and alcohol addiction.

Your body has wonderful systems that work non-stop for you. These systems are on your side! Why would you want to disrupt and sabotage their efforts by using drugs you do not need?

We all have the ability to reason! However, often when we are young, reasoning is clouded by our peers. We do not realize the stupidity of our actions until it is too late. Using illegal drugs is a selfish act. For a personal "high," you let down your parents, teachers and true friends. You forget the problems and shame that your actions cause. You just want to try it! Take a few minutes to think clearly before you do.

Smoking

Smoking draws smoke into your lungs from burning tobacco in a cigarette, cigar or pipe. Most of this smoke is then exhaled. Smoking adds carbon dioxide and nicotine to the air that we breathe. Your body also absorbs these products into the lungs and blood. Then this carbon-dioxide tainted blood is distributed, with oxygen, to all the cells in your body.

Smoke is made up of small solid particles of carbon and carbon dioxide that result from incomplete combustion. Carbon dioxide, a heavy gas, forms carbonic acid when dissolved in water. Nicotine is a poisonous, volatile alkaloid. It is the most active substance and the narcotic ingredient in tobacco. Nicotine is also used to manufacture insecticides.

Knowing this, what sane reason can you have for starting to smoke? Have you researched the effects of smoking on your body? Did your doctor, parents or teacher ask you to start smoking? Did any books or articles in any paper suggest smoking is good for you?

Usually, when you first try to smoke, you feel dizzy or sick to the stomach. However, for some of you, this is not a deterrent. You persist and gradually start inhaling. Wow, what an accomplishment! Once you start inhaling your body develops a craving for nicotine. Now you're hooked and it takes a lot of willpower to stop.

Sometimes it's useful to compare your body to well-known machine so you realize the damage you cause. Most of you are familiar with how a car engine operates. You realize that any engine requires oxygen to run. When you add carbon dioxide into the air intake of an engine, do you think it runs better? The answer is "No." Carbon dioxide does not help a car engine or your body.

Let's figure out the dollar cost of smoking. If you start smoking at age 15 (and, hopefully, live to age 65), you will have smoked for 50 years. Based on a reasonable inflation rate, your cost per day is about $5.00. The calculations are:

$5.00 x 365 days = $1,825.00 a year
$1,825.00 x 50 years = $91,250.00 total investment in smoking

However, if you invested this $1,825.00 a year at 6 percent compounded annually, in bonds, you would have $522,000.00 at age 65. Is smoking that important that you would give up $522,000.00, plus your health? Try this on your computer.

Here are some grizzly statistics on smoking.

According to the Centre for Disease Control and Prevention, in 1990 about 400,000 Americans died from smoke-related illnesses. As a comparison, statistics show that 292,000 Americans died in W.W.II. It appears tobacco is a greater enemy in peace time than the bombs and guns were during W.W.II.

Here is some more information from a reliable source. According to the World Organization and Imperial Cancer Research Fund, 3,000,000 people die from smoking each year worldwide. If the trend continues there will be 10,000,000 smoking-related deaths annually by the year 2020. The number of people alive today who will eventually be killed by tobacco is estimated at one-half billion.

Five percent of the women in the world live in the US, but the percentage of the world's women dying from smoking who live in the US is 50 percent. These are not encouraging bits of information for the smokers.

The National Centre of Health in the *New England Journal of Medicine* heralds some unsurprising news. Teens who smoke are more likely than their non-smoking peers to take up additional habits that may be hazardous to their health. They state that kids who light-up are 17 times more likely to use marijuana.

How can you, with your education and reasoning power, want to participate in something that you don't need and know to be wrong?

Teenage Pregnancy

Every day nearly 8,000 more children become sexually active. Every year more than 1,000,000 teenagers become pregnant. Every day 1,500 teenagers end their pregnancies. Every year about 250,000 teenagers contract syphilis, gonorrhea or herpes and a small, but tragic and growing number, get the HIV virus.

AIDS and herpes are incurable. The AIDS statistics from Centre for Disease Control as of October 1995 were:

- Number of cases in the US since 1981–501,310.

- Number who died–311,381.

- Cases reported in the last three years–247,741. Female deaths–43,383. As a comparison, during the Vietnam War (1965–1974) there were 47,244 American soldiers killed. This suggests AIDS is six times more deadly than war, and contracting it could be avoided.

Sexual intercourse is not the only way to get AIDS, but don't you think it is a foolish risk to take?

Sexual desire is one of our strongest basic drives. However, this urge can be controlled by the part of your brain that you have conscious jurisdiction over. Common sense, self-control and confidence are needed to overcome peer pressure.

Young people should learn the ABCs of healthy, honorable behavior the same way they learn their academic ABCs. Because you only live life once, it is important to learn this early while you are developing attitudes and habits.

There are many family health books that deal in depth with teenage pregnancies, sexual intercourse, sexual activity, rape and sexual abuse. It might be wise to read and study these teenage problems. The intent of this book is not to try to explain, justify or advise on these matters, but to make you aware of the merits of abstaining from sex until you are married.

Here are some reasons for both girls and boys to consider:

- If you are sexually active as a teenager, do you think you can be loyal to your partner when you marry?

- When you marry and one of the partners is experienced and the other is still a virgin, will this be a happy and lasting marriage for long?

- If you engage in sexual activity as a teenager, can you look forward to a true honeymoon when you marry?

- Having a baby when you are an adolescent is likely to put an end to your education, employment and school friendships.

- Most teenage pregnancies are unwanted. Unwanted children do not get the care and love they need. Children should be born in the confines of a happy marriage where they are wanted and loved.

- Teenage pregnancies bear a stigma to the teenager, their parents and the child.

- Boys cannot say that they had sex with a consenting teenager because consenting means over 18 years of age and free from alcohol and drugs.

- Boys who have a conscience should realize that by getting a girl pregnant, they have ruined her life and disgraced her and her parents. This is something that will be with them till their dying day.

Wouldn't it be a sign of honor and strength if parents could entrust their daughter to a boy on a date and count on him to act like a gentleman? Dancing cheek to cheek or kissing in the dark is also exciting and hurts no one.

There are so many sad experiences that prove teenage sexual activity is not in the best interests of those involved, but for some reason these mistakes are made over and over again.

Here is something that you may not have thought about when you started smoking, using alcohol, drugs or became sexually active. To hide your habit or habits you have to lie to parents and teachers. Remember small lies become big lies and lying could easily become part of your personality.

Problems and letdowns that will last the rest of your life can follow thoughtless mistakes. Your life can be happy and fruitful if you develop the common sense to learn to enjoy things that are good for you.

Nature's Laws and Man's Laws

Human beings are subject to two types of laws: Nature's Laws and Man's Laws. You need to take a few minutes and inspect these, noting the differences, and how they apply to your life.

The Laws of Nature are many. They apply in physics, science, chemistry, mathematics, reproduction of life, and hundreds of other fields. Some familiar ones are Newton's Law of Gravitation, Galileo's Law of Motion and Inertia, and Newton's Law of Motion and Force. You know what happens when you drop an object, or try to negotiate a sharp curve when travelling too fast, or try to stop at a stop sign when your speed is excessive, or when two objects in motion collide.

Nature's Laws are the same for all people, all colors and all nationalities. They are all based on *truth*. No one can cheat or lie to avoid these laws—they are self-policing and the penalties for breaking them can be quite severe.

Man's Laws may be defined as the sum of rules, conventions and observances for human conduct. A county, state, country, or international body levies penalties if these laws are violated and enforces them.

They are supposed to be the guide that determines the relationship of society as a whole, and individuals to one another.

You would not think of taking a journey to a strange country without a map or a guidebook. Everyone is expected to have some awareness of the laws of their country. To prevent penalties along the way, it is wise to learn to obey these laws.

Following is a comparison of the two laws—Man's and Nature's.

Man's laws are not self-policing and only a small portion of those who break these laws are ever penalized. Man's example to the young is sometimes not based on *truth*, but on ways to break minor laws and not get caught. Traffic violations and alcohol abuse are examples of this dishonesty. Because we are more influenced by Man's laws (or crime), they should bear closer inspection.

When you look at the costs of our justice system, it appears we spend more on punishment and revenge, than on prevention and proper education. We have not realized that an ounce of prevention is usually worth a pound of cure and that the proper time to use this preventative measure is at an early age. At this stage, character building, education on laws (both right and wrong) should be taught with a strong emphasis on individual responsibility.

Many children are born to the poor, the uneducated and young unwed mothers, who may not have the resources, knowledge or time to provide proper guidance. That is why some of these necessities should be taught in school at an early age. Many families do this at home, but if we were to double up on this type of education surely it would do nothing but good. It is an opportune time to prevent crime (law breaking) before it happens.

Today, imprisonment is often the penalty for lawbreakers. In the past, people were confined in dungeons. Often it seems that we have not advanced very much. Building more jails is not the answer. Wouldn't it be better to build more good schools with good instructors and teachers who could help build a personality that would not turn to crime. Even now, much credit for crime prevention should be given to police who get involved in communities and work to prevent crime.

Because of one mistake, a poor home life, or the lack of jobs, young teens and adults often turn to a life of crime. Many are repeat offenders who are incarcerated several times. Unfortunately, rather than being rehabilitated in the prison system, young offenders are often taught more about crime by hardened criminals. Many young people do not realize that once they have a prison record, jobs are hard to get. Even if they want to go straight, it is always a hard climb to attain any status in their community or elsewhere.

Unlike Nature's Laws that rely on *truth* alone, Man's Laws usually require a trial to determine the guilt and punishment of the offender. The outcome of a trial is sometimes dependent on color, ability of defense lawyers, witnesses and judges. You would think with all our technological advances, man could design a full proof lie detector. Then justice would be administered on *truth* and the only witness would be the defendant. Do you think the police would like such a detector if it were allowable in court? I am sure the answer would be "yes."

Lawyers, politicians, drug pushers, criminals and average people all say that lie detectors are not very reliable. But no one realizes that some of these detection devices, especially the voice lie detector, have not been upgraded for many years. There needs to be a demand to have money spent on research and development for this type of product.

Do we really want *truth*? What a deterrent it would be to teenage crime if everyone knew that they could not lie. What a deterrent it would be to drug dealers if they had to tell the *truth* when they are questioned by customs officials and police.

Gambling

Americans squander 55 billion dollars a year on games of chance. Gambling is a legal way of parting you from your money.

Gambling siphons money from those who can least afford it. People have always liked to gamble. Cities like Las Vegas prosper from this weakness. Gambling is big business and new casinos are appearing everywhere in the country.

Various organizations and states hold lotteries to raise money for education or sports. Most of the ticket buyers, however, are not interested in the lotto's objectives. Their interest lies in making a quick bonanza or fortune. Most could care less if lotto money provides additional facilities in a local school or is used to train athletes for the next Olympics.

The odds of winning a major lotto are several million to one. In fact, you have a greater chance of being struck by lightening than winning the lotto.

If you, the youth of our country, have the common sense and wisdom to spend your money on bonds, insurance or some other secure investments you could have a sure thing or "bonanza" waiting for you when you retire.

Wars

In international law, armed conflict between two or more governments is termed "international or public war." War between different parts or factions of the same nation is called "civil war."

Man has waged wars since ancient times. First, it was on a small scale, with stone weapons and clubs. Then they used steel swords and knives. Later, it was men on horses using swords and spears. In the 13th Century gunpowder was discovered. This resulted in the use of crude rifles, pistols and cannons.

Gradually more powerful explosives were made and "people killing machines" were harnessed to kill or destroy many people at a time. By "people killing machines," I mean automatic pistols, machine guns, land mines, powerful artillery, airplanes armed with bombs, tanks and cannons, submarines equipped with torpedoes, and armored ships.

During W.W.I there were about 8,500,000 people killed. During W.W.II this escalated to more than 35,000,000 deaths and a cost of more than a trillion dollars. Money had more value in the 1940s but you have to compare it to our peacetime national debt of more than five trillion dollars. Even in peacetime, it seems that a large portion of the debt is spent on building and designing weapons for defense.

Near the end of W.W.II. nuclear bombs were discovered with destructive powers equal to many thousands of tons of TNT. These bombs were stockpiled by the east and west and had the capability to destroy our civilization many times over. Fortunately, we are now demobilizing many of these terrible weapons and some progress is being made to control and ban them internationally.

Wouldn't it be wonderful if wars were banned as well? They do not bring happiness, even to the winners. They only bring grief, suffering, misery and death. We sometimes forget that the enemies that we shoot down or blow up are also human and have families that will mourn them. There must be a peaceful way to settle disputes in this day and age.

Wars are started for a variety of reasons and the ramifications are barbarous. Most of you have witnessed a serious or fatal car accident. Multiply your observations by thousands or millions and you will get an idea of what war is like. We are supposed to be civilized, educated, and have the power to reason and rationalize. However, man still engages in this terrible carnage.

Even today, disparity and poverty fuel our global security and the threat of war. Put simply, the global gap is widening between the "haves" and "have nots." These are the prime ingredients for more crime and terrorism. Surely we should have the wisdom to address and solve these problems before they lead us into another major war.

Here are some facts from the United Nations Human Development Report (1996).

- The income gap between the industrial world and the developing world has tripled over the last 30 years.

- 20 percent of the world's richest people have seen their share of global income rise 15 percent in the last 30 years.

- 20 percent of the world's poorest people have seen their share of global income fall to 1.4 percent from 2.3 percent in the same period.

- The assets of approximately 400 billionaires in the world exceed the combined income of the countries that have 45 percent of the world's population.

- 89 countries are now worse off economically than they were 10 years ago.

Hopefully, the "have" industrial nations will see the need to help poorer nations so they can realize some type of self-sufficiency. This would mean the industrial nations would have to continue educating the poorer nations in the areas of food production and realistic family planning so they can improve their economic growth.

Unfortunately, selling weapons to warring countries is still a multibillion-dollar a year business. If only mankind would consider the consequences and give these countries useful technology and food, instead of weapons.

For peace to prevail you will have to think of the less fortunate people on this planet, that we all live on, and share some of your prosperity

World Population

Here are some facts about the global population.

- 2,000 years ago the total population was estimated at 250,000,000.

- By 1960, the total population was about 3,000,000,000.

- By 1994, the total population was about 5,650,000,000.

- By 2010, anticipating an average growth rate of 1½ percent per year, the population will be 7,150,000,000. If the growth rate is held to 1 percent per year, the population would be 6,615,000,000.

- By 2050, at a 1½ percent growth rate per year, the global population will be close to 13 billion people.

Some researchers maintain that if all the people on Earth enjoyed a standard of living comparable to the US, our planet could only support 3,000,000,000 people. We have exceeded that number now and some of the "have not" nations have a problem just getting enough food to survive. Should we be more concerned with wise family planning and try to convince other countries to do the same? Think about the countries that have 1.5 or even 2 percent population growth per year.

One reason for the rapidly increasing population is the reduced mortality rate. This occurred because of the advances in medical technology.

Another reason is that for many centuries when populations were small and technology non-existent, "multiplying" was proper and encouraged. However, sometime soon we have to realize that this idea has to be drastically adjusted. We cannot keep doubling our population forever and expect there to be enough food, water and land available for everyone.

In 1996, the UN Food and Agriculture Organization released the following statistics and projections. It estimated that more than 800 million people worldwide were under nourished. Since 1990, the world population grew by 10 percent, but during that time the grain harvest increased by only 2.3 percent. Projections indicate that by 2025, world agriculture production must expand by 75 percent to match the population growth.

Many people prefer to dwell in cities or urban areas. Therefore, more of the fertile agricultural land is being used to accommodate new homes and industrial developments. Some years the available agricultural land is able to produce a slight surplus of food worldwide. However, your grandparents probably remember the drought of the 1930s, and what weather can do to expected food production. In the past, many rivers were damned to divert water for irrigation, but unfortunately we have run out of suitable rivers that can be used for this purpose.

Food is not the only problem. As factories and industrial projects become more efficient, they offer fewer jobs. But with an ever-increasing population jobs are a necessity. Can you imagine creating 70 million or 100 million new jobs every year worldwide? What about 100 years from now?

Perhaps there would be hope for long-term prosperity if we could dispense with grievances concerning land, language, politics and religion and replace them with co-operation, global thinking and fair solutions.

Most of you have access to a modern computer and the Internet. Do some research and ponder 50 or 100 years into the future. We have such a beautiful world, if only we realized it and did our share to keep it that way.

≈

Boy to his grandfather,
"Your generation didn't have all those social diseases,
what did you wear to have sex?
Grandfather, "A wedding ring."

≈

People who are hard working, smart, kind, honest and
likeable just seem to have all the luck.

≈

You have to do your own growing—no
matter how tall your father was.

≈

When you make your mark in the world,
watch out for those with erasers.

CHAPTER TEN

FUTURE PROBLEMS

Which Parent Are You?
"I got two A's," the small boy cried.
His voice was filled with glee.
His father very bluntly asked,
"Why didn't you get three?"
"Mom, I've got the dishes done,"
The girl called from the door.
Her mother very calmly said,
"Did you sweep the floor?"
"I've mowed the grass," the tall boy said,
"And put the mower away."
His father asked him, with a shrug,
"Did you clean off the clay?"
The children in the house next door
Seem happy and content.
The same things happen over there,
But this is how it went:
"I got two A's," the small boy cried.
His voice was filled with glee.
His father very proudly said, "That's great;
I'm glad you belong to me."
"Mom, I've got the dishes done,"
The girl called from the door.
Her mother smiled and softly said,
"Each day I love you more."
"I've mowed the grass," the tall boy said,
"And put the mower away."
His father answered with much joy,
"You've made my happy day."
Children deserve a little praise
For tasks they're asked to do,
If they're to lead a happy life,
So much depends on you.
                                            Badger Legionnaire

———

The best way to tell a woman's age is in a whisper.
                                            Earl Wilson

THE FUTURE

In the future, some of you will be leaders in your community, state and country. Moreover, you will be faced with serious problems that need positive and wise solutions.

Jet travel and modern communication systems have made the world smaller. You would think this would make life easier. And, in some cases, it has. However, the methods for solving world problems are complex and need frequent adjustment. We often find that trouble in a far-away place has the potential to become a worldwide problem if it is not resolved quickly. No nation is completely isolated. What one nation does, or does not do, affects the overall welfare of the world.

Even though you are not old enough to do anything now, you need to become interested—it will be your turn in a few years.

World Government

- Is our present world government (The United Nations) effective?

- After 50 years, should its structure be changed? Times change, problems change but for some reason we do not modify our constitutions to be in tune with the times.

- President Jefferson believed that constitutions should be fine-tuned every 10 or 20 years to keep up with progress. Would this be a good idea?

- Should the people on this planet consider themselves global citizens as well as citizens of their country?

- Should this government have a powerful, independent police force instead of a peacekeeping force, that could prevent disputes from turning into bloody wars?

- Should this government be able to ban war or the preparation for war?

- Should it eventually ban the use of lethal weapons?

- Should it get involved in preventing drug trafficking, corruption, money laundering, child labor and human rights violations?

- Should it get involved in a minimum required education for children worldwide?

- Should it have the power to force countries to gradually become democratic?

This is a tall order, but after all this is the 21st Century. We are supposed to be civilized and educated. When are we going to have peace in every corner of the world and make wars, poverty and human suffering things of the past?

Take time to research the League of Nations to see how badly it failed in preventing W.W.II. Hopefully, the United Nations can prevent all wars, including another World War.

Common Second Language

During the early centuries, Latin was the most common language. In the 17th Century, French was spoken in most of the European countries.

To change the languages of the world would be next to impossible. However, teaching everyone a common second language, such as English, could be useful.

A common second language would break the language barrier. All the nations' leaders could communicate without interpreters. This would enable them to settle their differences more easily and learn to cooperate more effectively in a world community. How easy it would be to use the Internet worldwide if it could be presented in one language.

Comparisons

During man's quest to develop a submarine he observed various inhabitants of the ocean. When he designed the airplane, he looked at birds for inspiration.

Maybe in your quest for an ideal system to govern the world, you should look to your body. Consider the power of the brain (that communicates instantly with every part of your body), the sophisticated distribution system, the immune system (or police force), and the teamwork of all the cells and components working together.

Does this sound familiar? Probably, it does! But consider whether your body would work as efficiently if it needed an interpreter to translate for all its systems?

Conclusion

I hope that you found this manual useful. I realize that some of the statistics are not very encouraging, but unfortunately they are true. It will be a challenge for you, the young generation, to improve on them and try to solve the problems of the future.

Please note that because of the availability of accurate statistics and surveys, the US was used as an example in many instances.

Remember time marches on with or without you. Everyday new problems arise that need to be carefully studied and corrected or adjusted. However, you need to realize that the problems of the 21st Century are usually very complicated and cannot be solved with Victorian remedies.

Here are some resolutions for the next Century:

- I will help my country and myself by staying healthy, strong and active, even as I grow old.

- I will recognize and disassociate myself from bad habits and attitudes.

- I will learn and practice safety habits at home, on the road, at work and at play, so that I can stay out of harm's way.

- I will prepare for marriage, even while I am young, so that when I do marry my commitment and love will last.

- I will recognize that proper education, proper character building and meaningful employment are humane ways of preventing crime.

- I realize that there is a need for careful family planning worldwide because there is not enough food, water or clean air to support our expanding population.

- I will do my part to look after our environment by maintaining nature's balance and finding ways to keep our air and water cleaner.

- I will practice conservation and recycling because I realize that our nonrenewable resources are limited. I recognize that the fossil fuels we use for transportation (especially air travel) will soon run out and that we should try to use them wisely.

- I realize that wars are cruel and barbarous and I will do my best to help devise a means to make them impossible.

- I hope that early in the next Century people's wisdom and intellect will advance to a point where the intentional killing of human beings is an ugly and shameful nightmare of the past.

- I will strive to improve our democratic type of government so it is a "true" model based on honesty, fairness, cooperation, honor, simplicity and good management with realistic human freedoms. Then, hopefully, it will be eagerly and peacefully embraced by most of the nations on the planet.

- Big Order! Impossible? Maybe not . . .

In closing, a simple reminder—You are all granted a little wisdom and a little time in this world. How prudently you develop the wisdom and balance the time will determine how long, how full, and how happy your life will be.

Judge yourself and others, not by material possessions, glamour or physical appearance, but by accepted standards of good human character and behavior.

CHAPTER ELEVEN

RECORDS

I wonder what today's younger generation will be able
to tell their children they did without?

Billy Graham

At Day's End
is anybody happier because you passed his way?
Does anyone remember that you spoke to him today?
The day is almost over, and its toiling time is through;
is there anyone to utter now a kindly word of you?
Can you say tonight, in parting with the day that's
  slipping fast,
That you helped a single brother of the many that you
  passed?

is a single heart rejoicing over what you did or said;
Does the man whose hopes were fading, now with
  courage look ahead?
Did you waste the day, or lose it? Was it well or sorely
  spent?
Did you leave a trail of kindness, or a scar of
  discontent?
As you close your eyes in slumber, do you think that
  God will say,
"You have earned one more tomorrow by the work
  you did today"?

John Hall

He enjoys much who is thankful for little; a grateful
mind is both a great and happy mind.

Thomas Secker

MEDICAL AND LIFESTYLE RECORD

If your records are correct, a doctor can get valuable information in diagnosing a current problem.

Vital Statistics

Full Name:

Date of Birth:

Place of Birth:

Blood Type:

Allergies, if any:

Do you wear a "Medic Alert" on your bracelet or necklace.   ☐ Yes   ☐ No

Health Problems, if any:

VISITS TO DOCTOR

Date	Doctor	Phone	Place

Reason & Results:

Date	Doctor	Phone	Place

Reason & Results:

Date	Doctor	Phone	Place

Reason & Results:

VISITS TO DOCTOR

Date	Doctor	Phone	Place

Reason & Results:

Date	Doctor	Phone	Place

Reason & Results:

Date	Doctor	Phone	Place

Reason & Results:

MEDICALS

Date	Doctor	Weight	Blood Pressure	Cholesterol

Problems, if any:

Date	Doctor	Weight	Blood Pressure	Cholesterol

Problems, if any:

Date	Doctor	Weight	Blood Pressure	Cholesterol

Problems, if any:

RECORD OF DENTAL EXAMINATIONS

Date	Doctor	Phone	Place

Procedures Performed:

Cost:

Date	Doctor	Phone	Place

Procedures Performed:

Cost:

Date	Doctor	Phone	Place

Procedures Performed:

Cost:

RECORD OF DENTAL EXAMINATIONS

Date	Doctor	Phone	Place

Procedures Performed:

Cost:

Date	Doctor	Phone	Place

Procedures Performed:

Cost:

Date	Doctor	Phone	Place

Procedures Performed:

Cost:

RECORD OF EYE EXAMINATIONS

Date	Doctor	Phone	Place

Results of Examination:

Cost:

Date	Doctor	Phone	Place

Results of Examination:

Cost:

Date	Doctor	Phone	Place

Results of Examination:

Cost:

MEDICAL DETAILS

Date	Doctor	Phone	Place
Pertaining to accident, disease, dental problems, operations or other problems.			

MEDICAL DETAILS

Date	Doctor	Phone	Place
Pertaining to accident, disease, dental problems, operations or other problems.			

NUTRITION (approximate average daily consumption)

Date	Age:	Actual Weight:	Desired Weight:
Daily Calories Required:		Actual Calories Consumed:	
Calories Obtained From Junk Food, Pop, etc.:			Fat g.:
Saturated Fat g.:	Cholesterol mg.:		Sodium mg.:
Antioxidants: Beta Carotene mg.:		Vitamin C mg.:	Vitamin E mg.:

Date	Age:	Actual Weight:	Desired Weight:
Daily Calories Required:		Actual Calories Consumed:	
Calories Obtained From Junk Food, Pop, etc.:			Fat g.:
Saturated Fat g.:	Cholesterol mg.:		Sodium mg.:
Antioxidants: Beta Carotene mg.:		Vitamin C mg.:	Vitamin E mg.:

Date	Age:	Actual Weight:	Desired Weight:
Daily Calories Required:		Actual Calories Consumed:	
Calories Obtained From Junk Food, Pop, etc.:			Fat g.:
Saturated Fat g.:	Cholesterol mg.:		Sodium mg.:
Antioxidants: Beta Carotene mg.:		Vitamin C mg.:	Vitamin E mg.:

NUTRITION (approximate average daily consumption)

Date	Age:	Actual Weight:	Desired Weight:
Daily Calories Required:		Actual Calories Consumed:	
Calories Obtained From Junk Food, Pop, etc.:			Fat g.:
Saturated Fat g.:	Cholesterol mg.:		Sodium mg.:
Antioxidants: Beta Carotene mg.:		Vitamin C mg.:	Vitamin E mg.:

Date	Age:	Actual Weight:	Desired Weight:
Daily Calories Required:		Actual Calories Consumed:	
Calories Obtained From Junk Food, Pop, etc.:			Fat g.:
Saturated Fat g.:	Cholesterol mg.:		Sodium mg.:
Antioxidants: Beta Carotene mg.:		Vitamin C mg.:	Vitamin E mg.:

Date	Age:	Actual Weight:	Desired Weight:
Daily Calories Required:		Actual Calories Consumed:	
Calories Obtained From Junk Food, Pop, etc.:			Fat g.:
Saturated Fat g.:	Cholesterol mg.:		Sodium mg.:
Antioxidants: Beta Carotene mg.:		Vitamin C mg.:	Vitamin E mg.:

EXERCISE

Date	Actual Weight:	Desired Weight:
No. of Times You Exercise Per Week:		
Approx. No. of Calories Burned With Exercise Per Week:		
Are You: Fit Moderately Fit: Unfit:		

Date	Actual Weight:	Desired Weight:
No. of Times You Exercise Per Week:		
Approx. No. of Calories Burned With Exercise Per Week:		
Are You: Fit Moderately Fit: Unfit:		

Date	Actual Weight:	Desired Weight:
No. of Times You Exercise Per Week:		
Approx. No. of Calories Burned With Exercise Per Week:		
Are You: Fit Moderately Fit: Unfit:		

EXERCISE

Date	Actual Weight:	Desired Weight:
No. of Times You Exercise Per Week:		
Approx. No. of Calories Burned With Exercise Per Week:		
Are You: Fit Moderately Fit: Unfit:		

Date	Actual Weight:	Desired Weight:
No. of Times You Exercise Per Week:		
Approx. No. of Calories Burned With Exercise Per Week:		
Are You: Fit Moderately Fit: Unfit:		

Date	Actual Weight:	Desired Weight:
No. of Times You Exercise Per Week:		
Approx. No. of Calories Burned With Exercise Per Week:		
Are You: Fit Moderately Fit: Unfit:		

MEDICATIONS RECORD

Date	Medication	Doctor	Reason	Cost

Immunizations	Date	Booster Shots
DTP diptheria, Tetanus and Whooping Cough)		
Poliomyelitis		
Measles and Mumps		
Rubella (German Measles)		
Tuberculosis		
Pneumonia Vaccination		

IMPORTANT PHONE NUMBERS

Name & Address	Phone/Fax

IMPORTANT PHONE NUMBERS

Name & Address	Phone/Fax

IMPORTANT PHONE NUMBERS

Name & Address	Phone/Fax

IMPORTANT PHONE NUMBERS

Name & Address	Phone/Fax

IMPORTANT PHONE NUMBERS

Name & Address	Phone/Fax

IMPORTANT PHONE NUMBERS

Name & Address	Phone/Fax

IMPORTANT PHONE NUMBERS

Name & Address	Phone/Fax